Max's Fez

and

Is Willa Bad?

PHASE 3

/x/y/
z/zz/

Level 3 – Yellow

Helpful Hints for Reading at Home

The graphemes (written letters) and phonemes (units of sound) used throughout this series are aligned with Letters and Sounds. This offers a consistent approach to learning whether reading at home or in the classroom.

HERE IS A LIST OF ALTERNATIVE PHONEMES FOR THIS PHASE OF LEARNING. AN EXAMPLE OF THE PRONUNCIATION CAN BE FOUND IN BRACKETS.

Phase 3			
j (jug)	v (van)	w (wet)	x (fox)
y (yellow)	z (zoo)	zz (buzz)	qu (quick)
ch (chip)	sh (shop)	th (thin/then)	ng (ring)
ai (rain)	ee (feet)	igh (night)	oa (boat)
oo (boot/look)	ar (farm)	or (for)	ur (hurt)
ow (cow)	oi (coin)	ear (dear)	air (fair)
ure (sure)	er (corner)		

HERE ARE SOME WORDS WHICH YOUR CHILD MAY FIND TRICKY.

Phase 3 Tricky Words			
he	you	she	they
we	all	me	are
be	my	was	her

PHASE 3

/x/y/ z/zz/

This book focuses on the phonemes /x/, /y/, /z/ and /zz/ and is a yellow level 3 book band.

Max's Fez
and
Is Willa Bad?

Written by
Kirsty Holmes

Illustrated by
Lynne Feng &
Julita Smiarowska

Can you make it through the maze to collect the letter z? How many objects beginning with z can you collect along the way?

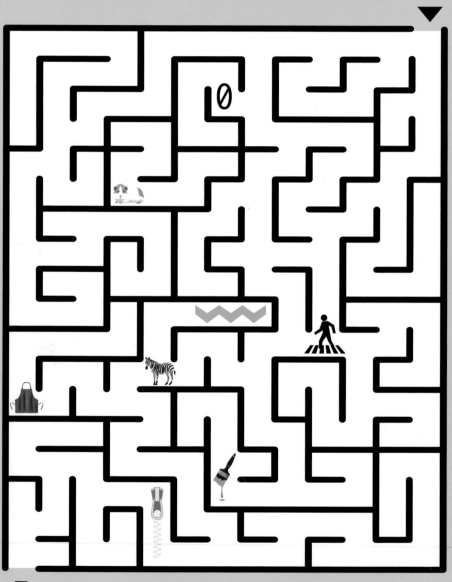

Z

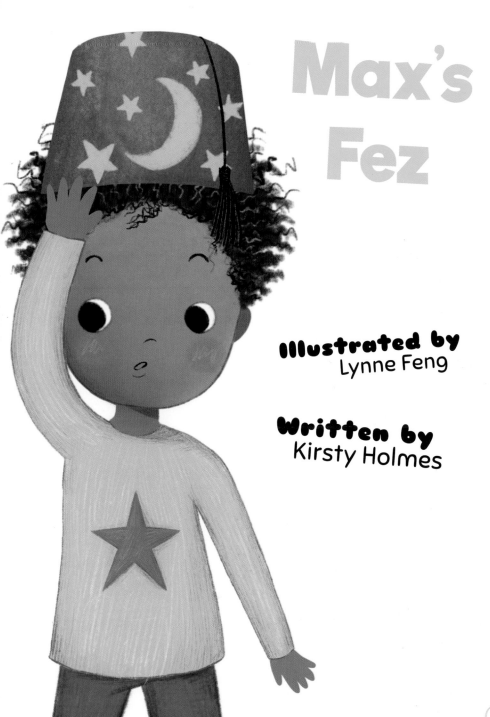

Max's Fez

Illustrated by
Lynne Feng

Written by
Kirsty Holmes

I am Max. This is my fez.

My fez fits my fuzz!

In my pot, I mix and mix and mix.
I tap my fez.

The pot is buzzing! The pot is fizzing!

It is an elf. The elf fits in the pot.

That is my fez! No, elf!

An elf in a fez? No! Bad elf!

Look at the fez. Buzz! Fizz! Look at the elf. Zip! Zap!

Zip zop zap, get the fez back!

The elf is sad. This is my fez. It fits my fuzz.

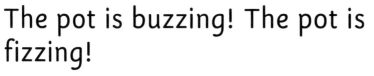

The pot is buzzing! The pot is fizzing!

An elf fez is in the pot!

Can you say this sound and draw it with your finger?

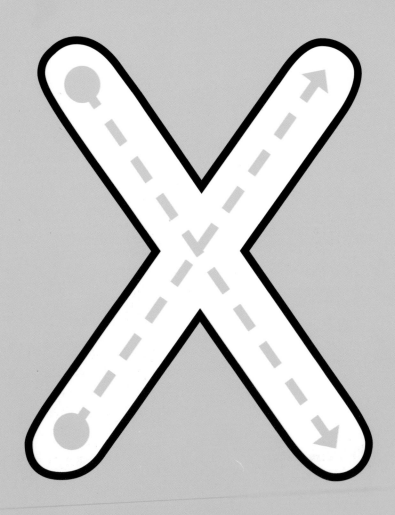

Is Willa Bad?

Written by
Kirsty Holmes

Illustrated by
Julita Smiarowska

It is Willa! Is Willa bad?

Willa has a velvet hat. And this is Hex, Willa's cat.

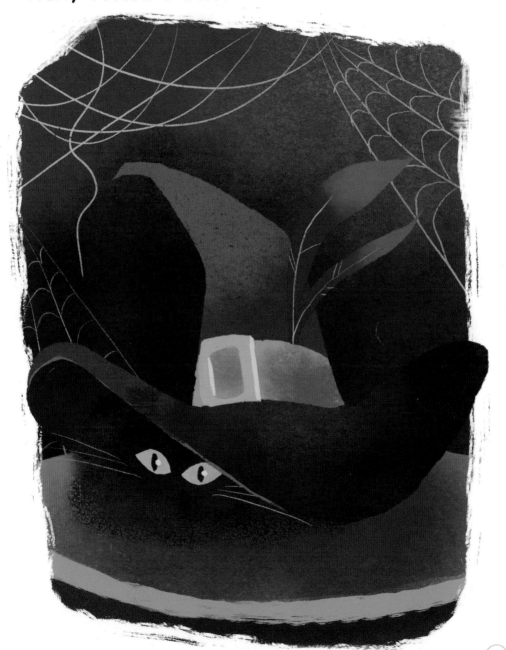

It is not a bad hat.

And he is not a bad cat! Is Willa bad?

Can you see webs and legs in Willa's jam?

That is not bad jam! It is good jam. Mmm!

Deepa needs Willa. Deepa is in pain.

"I can fix her leg with my webs! I will be back soon!"

Jack-Jack needs Willa. Jack-Jack is in pain.

"I can fix his wing. I will be quick."

Willa is not bad! Willa is...

… a good vet!

©2021 **BookLife Publishing Ltd.**
King's Lynn, Norfolk PE30 4LS

ISBN 978-1-83927-872-3

Max's Fez
Written by Kirsty Holmes
Illustrated by Lynne Feng
Is Willa Bad?
Written by Kirsty Holmes
Illustrated by Julita Smiarowska

An Introduction to BookLife Readers...

Our Readers have been specifically created in line with the London Institute of Education's approach to book banding and are phonetically decodable and ordered to support each phase of the Letters and Sounds document.

Each book has been created to provide the best possible reading and learning experience. Our aim is to share our love of books with children, providing both emerging readers and prolific page-turners with beautiful books that are guaranteed to provoke interest and learning, regardless of ability.

BOOK BAND GRADED using the Institute of Education's approach to levelling.

PHONETICALLY DECODABLE supporting each phase of Letters and Sounds.

EXERCISES AND QUESTIONS to offer reinforcement and to ascertain comprehension.

BEAUTIFULLY ILLUSTRATED to inspire and provoke engagement, providing a variety of styles for the reader to enjoy whilst reading through the series.

AUTHOR INSIGHT:
KIRSTY HOLMES

Kirsty Holmes, holder of a BA, PGCE, and an MA, was born in Norfolk, England. She has written over 60 books for BookLife Publishing, and her stories are full of imagination, creativity and fun.

PHASE 3
/x/ /y/
z/ /zz/

This book focuses on the phonemes /x/, /y/, /z/ and /zz/ and is a yellow level 3 book band.